CONTENTS

INTRODUCTION

Hawaii's coastlines include wave-washed rocky shores and ledges, sandy
beaches, exposed tidepools, and shallow reef flats. Each of these habitats
provides homes for many of Hawaii's most beautiful and interesting animals
— the marine invertebrates. Invertebrates include many familiar seashore
animals such as crabs, sea urchins, sea snails, and coral. Although widely
diverse, the one characteristic they share is the absence of a backbone.
The name "invertebrate" means "without vertebrae". It takes little in
the way of equipment or knowledge to become acquainted with this
great variety of marine life; however, it is important to be "safety"
conscious — conscious of both your safety and the safety of the animals
you are discovering.

SAFETY

"Never turn your back to the sea" is an old Hawaiian saying, learned through hard-won experience, and most applicable when exploring near an area of wave action. Potential hazards other than surf are certain forms of marine life. Be sure to protect your hands and feet with gloves and shoes when reef walking or tidepooling. Employ the buddy system when exploring; the shared experience is safer and much more fun.

GENERAL HINTS

Check a tide table or tide calendar for the time of low tide if you are reef walking or tidepooling. A "loc box" is a great help for seeing clean through the water. Clear plastic cu or zip-loc bags are handy for puttir small animals in for closer observati Try reef walking at night with a bright light; some animals are seen only after dark.

CONSERVATION

Many of the animals you will find are fragile and sensitive to removal from water. Handle them as little and as gently as possible. After you are through, replace them as they were. If it was necessary to move or overturn a rock, replace it as you found it. Animals and plants living on the undersurface of a rock usually cannot tolerate prolonged exposure to waves, light, and air, while those on the top need them. Be sure not to break off coral heads expecting them to live if you put them back. They need their firmly attached base to hold them above the silt and sand and to keep them from rolling around in the waves.

INTRODUCTION
TO HAWAIIAN WATERS

Marine animals, both fish and invertebrates, generally have young that spend their early life floating or drifting in the ocean's currents. Animals and plants that live in this way are called "plankton" from the Greek word *planktos* meaning "to wander". These "planktonic larvae", as the young are called during this stage, usually do not resemble their parents and are adapted to live in a drifting mid-water environment rather than a swimming or bottom-dwelling one. They are usually small and clear with oil droplets or spines to help them float.

Many planktonic animals and plants are able to drift across expanses of open ocean, coming to rest on distant shores. Ancestors of animals that have settled Hawaii's waters came mainly from the southwestern Pacific. Some forms which arrived here evolved into new species found nowhere else in the world. Hawaii shares its affinity with the tropical Indo-Pacific, yet because of its isolation from other island groups, supports a marine fauna unique in the world.

ZONATION

The portion of the shoreline which is alternately covered and exposed by the tidal change is called the intertidal or littoral zone. This zone can be subdivided into several subzones, and different animals and plants will be found in distinct subzones depending on environmental conditions occurring there.

The highest or "splash" zone is that area wetted only by wave splash. Beneath this is the "upper intertidal" zone which is covered by water at high tide. Next is found the "middle intertidal" zone which is covered during moderate tides. The "lower intertidal" zone is covered most of the time and exposed only during low tides. The "sub-tidal" zone is never exposed. Although the subtidal is usually thought of as the deeper water at the edge of the shoreline, it also includes many tidepools.

Environmental conditions are most harsh in the upper intertidal and splash zones as these areas are left exposed to sun and rain more often than the lower zones. Consequently, fewer animals are found there. Zonation, then, is the horizontal distribution of animals and plants according to environmental conditions.

SPONGES • Phylum Porifera

Sponges are the simplest animals composed of more than one cell. They have no nervous system or muscles, and as adults are permanently attached. Their bodies are supported by a skeletal matrix which may consist of tiny hard rods called spicules, or of a flexible network called spongin, or both. The body of a sponge is perforated by several large openings and many tiny pores. Inside, the sponge contains many internal canals which are lined by tiny hair-like structures. The beating of these hairs draws a current of water into the sponge through the small holes. Sponges are filter feeders, obtaining nourishment from plankton which is drawn into the body with the seawater.

Sponges usually feel soft and spongy to the touch, but caution is advised: many sponges contain a substance irritating to human skin. Sponges are commonly found under rocks in shallow water. Those shown here are 1 to 2 inches across.

Phylum COELENTERATA
Sea Anemones · Corals · Jellyfish

This is a large group containing some very common and important animals. Two basic body forms found within this phylum are called the "polyp" and the "medusae". A sea anemone (opposite) characterizes the polyp form with an attached cylindrical stalk capped by a crown of tentacles. A mouth lies within the center of the tentacles and is the only opening to the gut. The jellyfish (below) characterizes the medusa plan. This is a swimming bell-shaped animal with the mouth and tentacles facing downward. A character shared by these seemingly dissimilar animals is the presence of tentacles containing stinging structures (nematocysts). These are used for food capture and protection. (*Aiptasia pulchella*, left; *Phyllorhiza punctata*, below.)

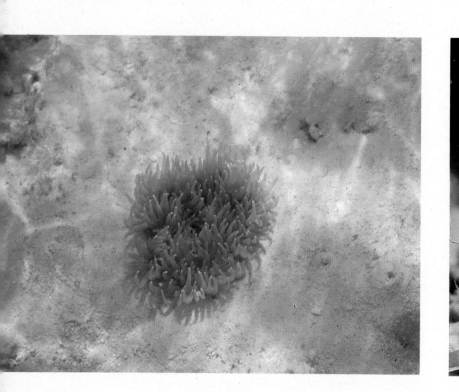

SEA ANEMONES

Hawaiian sea anemones are generally found attached to rocks or hard reef surfaces and are often less than an inch across. Two notable exceptions are the sand-dwelling anemone *Antheopsis papillosa* (left), and the shell-dwelling anemone *Calliactis polypus* (above). The large, white, sand-dwelling anemone may reach 6 inches across the disc and is found on sand-covered reef flats in Kaneohe Bay and in shallow sand-filled crevices in reefs and tidepools on the windward side of Oahu. *Calliactis polypus* lives symbiotically with hermit crabs of the genus *Dardanus*. The hermit crab is able to transfer these anemones from rocks to shells, or from shell to shell. This relationship benefits the anemone by providing it with transportation and perhaps food, and in turn its stinging cells help protect the crab from predators. These cells are found in the tentacles and in strings released from the body wall. This hermit crab reaches 10 inches in length and may be found on shallow reef flats at night.

ZOANTHIDS

Zoanthids are clusters of anemone-like animals which live either on hard surfaces or in sand, and are often seen in shallow, wave-washed areas. The tissue shared by colony members may extend all the way up to the small tentacles, as in *Palythoa tuberculosa* (below), or may be only around the base of the colony, as seen in the species of *Zoanthus* (opposite page). Zoanthid tentacles are generally very small, leading biologists to believe that these animals may gain some nourishment from the presence of symbiotic algae found in their tissues.

Two species of zoanthids are toxic, and one is so strong that the Hawaiians call it *limu-make-o-Hana*, or "deadly seaweed of Hana". Spear tips were reportedly dipped in this zoanthid so that even a slight wound caused by the spear could be fatal. Neither toxic species is common around the islands. Zoanthid individuals are often about a half an inch in diameter, but colonies may be two feet across.

17

CORALS

Corals, like the preceding zoanthids, are basically colonies of anemone-like animals, called "polyps", joined together by common tissue. However, corals secrete a skeleton while zoanthids do not. The common shallow water stony corals secrete skeletons of calcium carbonate (limestone), while other kinds of corals such as sea fans and precious corals secrete skeletons of other materials. The living portion of the colony is only a thin layer of pigmented tissue covering the surface of the hard skeleton. Each individual polyp sits in a separate cup. (Species shown is *Tubastraea coccinea.*)

CORAL ECOLOGY

The most common, fastest growing corals in shallow water are called "reef-building" corals. They differ from other forms of coral by the presence of plant cells within their tissues. The coral and algae have a symbiotic relationship in which each benefits from chemical substances produced or used by the other. Since the algal cells must have sunlight in order for photosynthesis to occur, corals which contain algal cells can survive only to depths which sunlight can penetrate.

The amount of light reaching the coral can be reduced by factors other than depth. A green bubble algae *Dictyosphaeria cavernosa* which is common in Kaneohe Bay, Oahu, grows over living coral and eventually smothers it by blocking out light and food. Excess silt in the water caused by heavy rains or dredging can also block light penetration and smother corals.

CORAL ZONATION

Wave action is important in determining where a coral is able to grow, some corals doing well in wave-battered areas, other more fragile forms requiring calmer water. The cauliflower coral *Pocillopora meandrina* (opposite, bottom) grows well in areas of moderate wave action and is usually the dominant coral on reef slopes in depths less than 10 feet. The yellow or brown lobe coral *Porites lobata* (opposite, top), also does well in shallow areas but is dominant in the zone just below the cauliflower coral. Finger coral *Porites compressa* (below) requires calmer water. It will be found in relatively deep water on a reef slope exposed to wave battering or in shallow water in protected bays such as Kaneohe Bay, Oahu, and Honolua Bay, Maui. It is characteristically found in the zone beneath lobe coral.

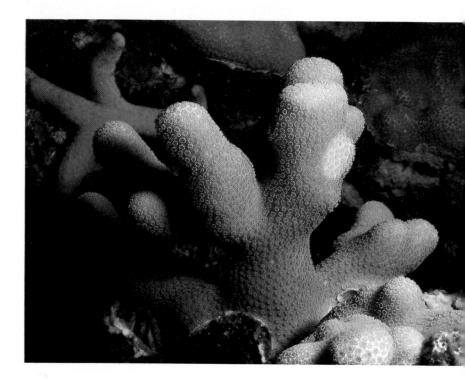

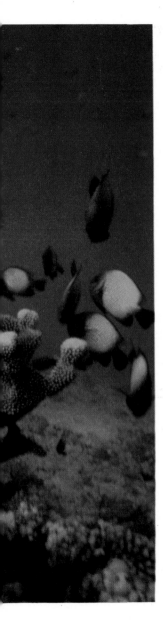

The branches of coral heads protect many kinds of animals. A school of damselfish hovers over a large *Pocillopora eydouxi* head, ready to move in closer if threatened (opposite). The red and white-spotted *Trapezia* crab (below) lives only in coral heads, along with several other species of crustaceans. Animals living permanently within coral heads are often spotted, a pattern which blends in with the light and shadows cast by the irregular surface of the coral skelton.

JELLYFISH

A jellyfish is basically an upside-down sea anemone. The characteristic central mouth and ring of tentacles are there, but beneath the bell rather than on top. The gently pulsating bell propels the body through the water, while trailing tentacles and oral arms gather food. Some jellyfish rely on stinging cells in the tentacles to stun prey, while others entrap small food particles with a mucus secretion.

Jellyfish are often confused with the Portuguese-man-o'-war, but differ from them in having a fleshy swimming bell rather than a gas-filled float. (*Cephea cephea*, above).

OCTOCORALS

The octocorals occur in abundance on the shallow reefs of more tropical waters, but are poorly represented in Hawaii. Polyps of this group are characterized by eight feathery tentacles. *Sinularia abrupta* (above) has the appearance of a smooth, hard coral, but is soft to the touch. The shallowest it occurs is about 15 feet. *Anthelia edmondsoni* (opposite) can be seen in tidepools or in the shallow subtidal. The polyps are tiny, but may cover parts of rocks with a soft lavender mat.

HYDROIDS

Hydroids are plant-like colonies of small animals related to sea anemones. Each colony consists of a center stem with side branches covered with polyps. The insides of the stems and branches are hollow, allowing food and wastes to flow through the colony. Some of the polyps are supplied with potent stinging cells strong enough to cause a burning sensation in humans. Because of the plant-like appearance and stinging tentacles, hydroids are sometimes called "stinging *limu*" in Hawaii (*limu*=seaweed). (Below, *Halocordyle disticha.*)

PORTUGUESE-MAN-O'-WAR

Painfully venomous, the Portuguese-man-o'-war *Physalia physalis* is easily recognized by the bluish bubble that keeps it afloat at the ocean's surface. Trailing beneath the water are elastic, stinging cell-laden tentacles that discharge tiny venomous barbs into unwary prey. Like the hydroids, the Portuguese-man-o'-war is a colonial form rather than a single animal; its various members perform separate functions such as food capture, feeding, and reproduction.

The Portuguese-man-o'-war is part of the "wind-drift" community which consists of animals that live on the surface of the ocean far out at sea. Other members of this community include the snail *Janthina fragilis,* and the nudibranch *Glaucus atlanticus,* both of which are reported to feed on the Portuguese-man-o'-war. After storms or periods of strong winds these animals are found along Hawaii's beaches. Each is about an inch or two in length.

WIND DRIFT COMMUNITY

The violet shell *Janthina fragilis* (above) floats at the water's surface by secreting a mass of bubbles which can often be seen on beached specimens. The nudibranch *Glaucus atlanticus* has a flattened body with wing-like projections which help it float on the water's surface. It is able to feed on the Portuguese-man-o'-war without discharging the stinging cells. These cells are then stored by the nudibranch in the body extensions and used for its own defense.

FLATWORMS

Phylum
Platyhelminthes

Flatworms can be flam-
boyantly colored with
stripes and spots or so
drab and well camouflaged
they are seldom seen.
They are often confused
with nudibranchs (sea
slugs), but are flatter and
lack the frilly projections
on the back that most
nudibranchs bear. Flat-
worms do not move by
means of muscular con-
tractions as snails do, but
by beating tiny rows of
hairs (cilia) in a trail of
mucus. They are effective
predators on animals such
as snails and oysters and
may be found living under
rocks in shallow reef
areas. They are normally
about an inch in length.

SEGMENTED WORMS
Phylum Annelida

Featherduster worm, spaghetti worm,
Christmas tree worm, fireworm: these
are the descriptive names of some
common marine segmented worms. The
bodies of these worms are ringed by
grooves outside and are divided inside by
partitions. Each segment bears spines or
bristles along both sides which aid in
locomotion, protection, anchoring or
burrowing, depending on each species'
lifestyle. The segmented worms live in
many different kinds of habitats.
(*Sabellastarte sanctijosephi,* left)

34

FIREWORMS

Fireworms bear many white bristles along their sides
which can cause irritation and itching when touched.
This type of worm is often found on the undersides of
rocks in shallow water and does not make a tube or
burrow. They feed on very small animals and have well-
developed eyes and other sense organs for searching for
prey. They range in size from 2 to 6 inches.

FEATHERDUSTER WORMS

The featherduster worms live in protective tubes and can be seen in tidepools and on shallow reef flats. While the body is hidden from view, a large fan projects from the tube to gather food and absorb oxygen. The fan is sensitive to both light and water motion, and the worm can withdraw it rapidly when alarmed. Large fans may be 5 inches across. (Below, *Sabellastarte sanctijosephi.*)

SPAGHETTI WORMS

Some tube worms use tentacles for food gathering. The cluster of long white tentacles reaching 2 to 3 feet in length and often seen in wave-washed tidepools belongs to the spaghetti worm *Lanice conchilega*. The body of the worm lies buried under rocks and sand. Cilia-lined grooves run the length of the tentacles and transport organic particles to the mouth. Hawaiians reportedly used the spaghetti worm medicinally, and recent research at the University of Hawaii has explored its anti-cancer properties.

Thelepus setosus (opposite) is shown out of its tube with a small commensal crab. This worm is only about 2 inches in length.

CHRISTMAS TREE WORM

Spirobranchus giganteus, the Christmas tree worm, lives inside coral heads. Each worm has two brilliantly colored spiraled fans which are used to capture food. A hard spiny attachment, the operculum, serves as a door to the tube, protecting the worm from predators. The worm builds a hard calcareous tube within the living coral head. Somehow, this worm can survive surrounded by living coral tissue without being overgrown by it. Each spiral fan is about ½ inch across.

MOLLUSKS

The mollusks, one of the largest groups of marine invertebrates
in Hawaii, include snails, slugs, clams, oysters, chitons, octo-
puses and squid. The Hawaiian mollusks vary greatly in shape,
size, and lifestyle, but have some general characteristics in
common. Their bodies are unsegmented; they have a muscular
foot used in locomotion; they have thin folds of tissue called
the mantle enclosing the body and secreting the shell; in most
there is a distinct head end with eyes and sensory tentacles.
Many mollusks feed by scraping organic material with a hard
spiny tongue called a radula. Mollusks may have either one,
two or eight shells, but some like the nudibranchs and octo-
puses, have none. Mollusks were of great importance in old
Hawaii and were used for food, jewelry, tools, fishing lures,
and in rituals. The general term used for mollusks is *pupu*.
(Below, the tun shell *Tonna perdix*)

MOLLUSKS OF THE ROCKY INTERTIDAL

CHITONS

The shell of a chiton is made of 8 plates arranged in a row and encircled by a tough girdle. Chitons seldom leave their homesite except to forage for algae which they scrape off with their radula. The largest Hawaiian chiton *Acanthochiton viridis* can reach 1½ inches in length and is common on the wave-washed limestone beaches near Barber's Point and Kahuku, Oahu. Other small chitons can be found living under rocks in the intertidal zone. The Hawaiian name for chitons is *pupu pe'elua* which means caterpillar shell.

PERIWINKLES

Small pointed-shell snails of the genus *Littorina* live in the relatively dry splash zone. Since drying out is a problem in this habitat, these snails conserve moisture by sealing their shell shut with the operculum and gluing it to the rock with mucus. The vertical movements of these snails during feeding follow a tidal rhythm which persists even after they are removed from the shoreline. One Hawaiian name for these snails is *pupu kolea*.

NERITES

The round, black *Nerita picea*, called *pipipi* in Hawaiian, live a little closer to the water than do the periwinkles but still high in the intertidal. They are often found in aggregations under ledges or in depressions. Both the periwinkles and nerites were used as food by the Hawaiians. Small shallow water hermit crabs are often found inhabiting the empty shells of both nerites and periwinkles.

LIMPETS

In Hawaii limpets are known as *opihi* and are a highly prized delicacy. This cone-shaped mollusk inhabits the surge zone of the islands' roughest coastlines and can be very dangerous to collect. Superbly adapted for its environment, the *opihi* has a low profile and broad base which keep the center of gravity low, along with a very strong muscular foot for firm attachment to the rocks. *Opihi* pickers must catch their prey unawares, for once the snail has clamped down his shell, there is little hope of removing it. (Opposite, *Cellana exarata,* the "black foot" *opihi.*)

"FALSE OPIHI"

The false *opihi, Siphonaria normalis,* bears a superficial resemblance to the true *opihi* but differs from them in several ways. The false *opihi* belongs to the siphon shell family, a group of snails that have adapted to live out of the water much of the time. These snails can be found high in the intertidal on rocks and limestone, whereas true *opihi* are usually found in the middle intertidal and lower. False *opihi* are smaller (½ to ¾ inch across), often whitish, and bitter to the taste.

COWRIES

Cowries have lovely rounded, glossy shells that are prized by shell collectors. The mantle, the organ that secretes the shell, can also completely cover it in this group. This keeps the shell highly polished and also serves to camouflage it, as the mantle coloration often blends with the habitat of the cowry. The snake's head cowry *Cypraea caputser-pentis* (above) is Hawaii's commonest shallow water cowry. It is about an inch long and can be found under rocks or in depressions in the rocky intertidal zone. The Hawaiian name for cowries is *leho*. (Upper right, *Cypraea gaskoini*, lower right, *C. maculifera*).

46

CONE SHELLS

Cone shells are predators on other marine animals. Some species of cones eat fish, others eat mollusks, while still others eat worms. These slow moving carnivores are able to subdue their prey by shooting them with a venomous harpoon. The harpoon is a modified radula that is released from the proboscis at the narrow end of the shell. The characteristics of the venom differ depending upon the type of prey. A fish-eating cone has a venom which is more harmful to humans than that of a worm-eater. (Below, *Conus lividus*.)

Conus textile, the "cloth-of-gold" cone, preys upon other mollusks. The photograph below was taken immediately after it had stabbed a pimpled basket shell with the venomous harpoon. The pink proboscis wields the harpoon, while the red-tipped siphon serves to draw water in over the gills. Cone shells should be handled only from the broad end, and always with caution. Many kinds of cones can be found in shallow water and may be ¾ of an inch to several inches in length.

TUBE-SHELL SNAILS

Snails of the family Vermetidae build hard calcium carbonate tubes which they cement to reefs, rocks and other hard surfaces. The larges most commonly seen species, *Serpulorbis variabilis* (left), lives alon(wave-washed shores and builds a spiraled tube which is usually 2 to 3 inches across. Another smaller species (¼ inch across), *Dendropoma gregaria* (below), forms dense aggregations and covers large areas of the reef a Diamond Head Beach Park and Fort Kamehmeha reef, Oahu. These snails feed by extending a mucus net which traps plankton and is then drawn in an swallowed.

BIVALVES

Bivalves are mollusks with two shells and include clams, oysters, and mussels. A common, small (½ inch) mussel, *Brachidontes cerebristriatus* (left), occurs in dense aggregations on shallow limestone reefs such as those at Fort Kamehameha and Diamond Head Beach Park, Oahu. Other common bivalves found attached to the undersides of stones in shallow water belong to the genus *Isognomen* and are 1 to 2 inches in length. These are related to the pearl oysters and have a mother-of-pearl inner surface.

SEA HARES

Sea hares are marine snails with a reduced or absent shell. They gain their common name from the large paired earlike projections usually found on the head, and from their algae-eating habits. Sea hares are often found in the intertidal zone among the algae on which they feed or under rocks, and at certain times of the year may appear in great numbers. Some sea hares reach a foot in length, but most are from 1 to 4 inches. Several species release a purple fluid when disturbed. (Opposite, *Stylocheilus longicauda,* below, *Aplysia dactylomela.*)

NUDIBRANCHS

The colorful and delicate nudibranchs are also called sea slugs, because like land slugs, they are snails without shells. The shell normally covers the gills of a snail, but in dorid nudibranchs these are exposed and encircle the anus *(Hexabranchus sanguineus,* below). In fact, the term "nudibranch" means "naked gills". Eolid nudibranchs lack gills, but have a row of cerata along the back which contain extensions of the digestive tract *(Spurilla neopolitana,* upper right). Nudibranchs with cerata often feed on colenterates and are able to ingest the stinging cells without discharging them. These stinging cells are then transported to the tips of the cerata where the nudibranch uses them for its own defense. Some nudibranchs bear neither gills nor cerata on the dorsal surface *(Phyllidia varicosa,* lower right). Many nudibranchs can be found in shallow water and are often less than an inch in length, however, the Spanish dancer (below) may reach 10 inches in length.

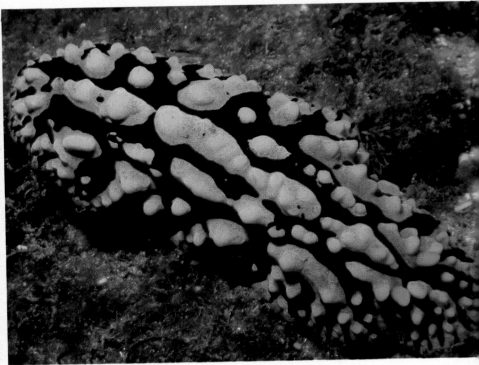

ECHINODERMATA

Sea Urchins · Sea Stars
Brittle Stars · Sea Cucumbers

Although members of this large group of animals bear little superficial resemblance to each other, there are unifying characteristics. One of the most important is the presence of "tube feet" such as these on the "crown-of-thorns" sea star (below). Each tube foot is an extension of the inner body wall that is operated by water pressure in a closed "plumbing" system. Generally, each tube foot ends in a suction cup. Tube feet are used for locomotion and attachment.

SEA URCHINS

The sea urchins are among the most common shallow water marine invertebrates in Hawaii. Some urchins have venomous spines, but most are harmless to man. Sea urchins have a hard skeleton called a "test" which encloses the soft body parts and the complex feeding structure called "Aristotle's lantern", so named because Aristotle described it as resembling a Greek lantern. The broken-open sea urchin (above) shows the Aristotle's lantern in the center along with the muscles which operate it. The yellow material is the edible part of a sea urchin, which is developing eggs or sperm. The five areas of brownish material house the tube feet which extend to the outside through holes in the test.

VENOMOUS URCHINS

The early Hawaiians divided the sea urchins into several major groupings. *Wana* was their name for the venomous variety. These urchins have long, slim, needle-like spines which may be white, black, or white and black banded. There may also be an iridescent blue or green sheen to the spines. The *wana* have two kinds of spines, the long, hollow primaries, and the shorter, finer, venom-tipped secondaries.

Diadema paucispinum (opposite) has the longest spines of the three species of *wana* known to occur in Hawaii. The two shorter spined *wana, Echinothrix calamaris* and *E. diadema,* are difficult to tell apart in the field. Both have black and white banded spines in the young stages, and some banding may persist as the animal matures. However, if the bubble-like anal cone in the center top of the urchin is exposed, it is spotted in *E. calamaris* (below) and black in *E. diadema.* If the animal is dead, it is possible to tell the two apart by rubbing fingers down a primary spine from tip to base. If the fingers slide down easily the urchin is *E. diadema;* if they do not, it is *E. calamaris.*

ROCK BORING URCHINS

The Hawaiian name *ina* includes the small, rock boring urchins common in the intertidal zone. The two species found in Hawaii are the light-colored *Echinometra mathaei* (opposite and above) and the black *E. oblonga* (not shown). They are not venomous and have the ability to make protective burrows in rock and reef. It is not totally understood how they erode the rock surface to make their homes. They live in a variety of habitats and are as likely to be found in depressions on a wave-washed bench as they are under rocks in quiet near-shore waters. These urchins generally stay in one area and eat algae which is caught on the spines.

ARMORED URCHINS

These two seemingly dissimilar urchins have two unusual features in common: some or all of the spines on the upper surface are short and table-like, forming an armor plating over the body; and the spines around the edge and underside of the body are broad and flattened to aid in clinging to the reef. In some parts of Hawaii these urchins are grouped collectively as *ha'uke'uke,* although this name often refers to just the shingle urchin (below). The slate-pencil urchin *Heterocentrotus mammillatus* (left) may live either in exposed or protected habitats among coral and rocks. The shingle urchin *Colobocentrotus atratus* (below) lives only along wave-washed shores where it takes the full force of the surf. Like the *opihi,* its flattened, broadly based shape is an adaption for survival in this harsh environment.

COLLECTOR URCHIN

The round, black, short-spined urchin *Tripneustes
gratilla* has a habit of collecting debris on its top.
Hāwa'e, as it is called in Hawaiian, is a wandering
species reportedly without a homesite on the reef. Adult
specimens average about 5 inches in diameter and are
common in the shallow subtidal zone. Young specimens
are sometimes seen in tidepools. The tube feet are easily
seen on this species because of the short spines.

COMMENSALISM

Several species of shrimp live among the spines of various kinds of sea urchins. *Stegopontonia commensalis* (below) sits in a head down position on a single primary spine of a venomous sea urchin. Its color ranges from purple in the young stages to black in the adult. The white line serves to break up its silhouette making it less visible to predators.

Sea stars are not plentiful in the intertidal zone in Hawaii, but *Linckia multifora* is sometimes seen in the shallow subtidal zone. This sea star has an interesting means of asexual reproduction — it can break off an arm which then grows into a complete starfish, while the individual that dropped the arm grows a replacement. It is not unusual to find specimens of *L. multifora* in all growth stages. Individuals with one long and four short arms are called "comets" because of their resemblance to a shooting star (opposite). Specimens average 6 inches across.

CROWN-OF-THORNS SEA STAR

The crown-of-thorns sea star *Acanthaster planci* is found below the intertidal zone and is well known for its habit of feeding on living coral. Here it is seen with the orange coral *Tubastraea coccinea* under a ledge. The characteristic large, sharp spines of the crown-of-thorns can cause a painful wound and should be avoided. Between the spines are small, finger-like projections called "papulae". These are extensions of the inner body wall and are used in respiration. Small pincers can be seen in the lower part of the photograph. These help protect the delicate papulae. The crown-of-thorns average 12 inches across, with spines of about 1 inch in length.

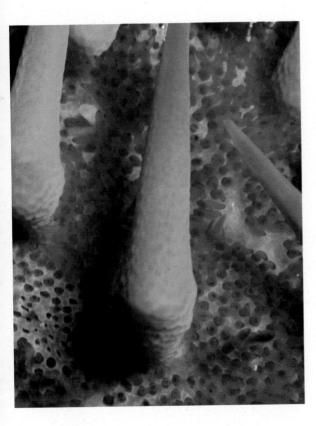

CUSHION STAR

Culcita novaeguineae is a large sea star, usually about 10 inches across. It is shaped like a plump cushion and is often seen while snorkeling. It eats coral, but does little damage as it rarely eats an entire colony at one sitting. The coral is then able to regenerate the lost polyps.

BRITTLE STAR

Brittle stars bear a superficial resemblance
to sea stars, but differ from them in several
ways: in a brittle star the distinction between
the arm and central disc is clear, while in a
sea star the two blend together; the arms of
a brittle star are flexible, while those of a
sea star are not; and brittle stars have no
suction cups on their tube feet as sea stars
do. While sea stars usually live exposed on
the reef, brittle stars live under rocks, in
holes in rocks, in sponges and other similarly
protected places. When exposed or disturbed
they are able to move quickly to a new
hiding place by using their flexible, spiny
arms. Brittle stars vary greatly in size but
generally range between 1 and 12 inches
between arm tips. They are common in
shallow water. (Above, *Ophiocoma pica.*)

SEA CUCUMBERS

Many kinds of sea cucumbers occur in Hawaii, and they come in an array of colors and consistencies. Most Hawaiian sea cucumbers are firm bodied, such as *Holothuria atra* (left) and some are used as food by Hawaii's various cultures. These firm-bodied species have many tube feet along the ventral surface which are used for attachment. Other kinds of sea cucumbers are thin bodied and lack tube feet. These are often mistakenly called "sea worms". One species, *Ophiodesoma spectabilis* (below), is very common in Kaneohe Bay, Oahu. The Hawaiian name for sea cucumbers is *loli*.

The number and strength of the tube feet of an echinoderm reflect its life-style. The brown and white speckled sea cucumber *Actinopyga mauritiana* (right) clings tenaciously to rocks in the wave washed intertidal zone, surviving in a more exposed habitat than any other Hawaiian sea cucumber. The brown-banded *Holothuria pervicax* lives under stones in the intertidal zone, protected from strong wave action. Accordingly, its attaching ability is slight.

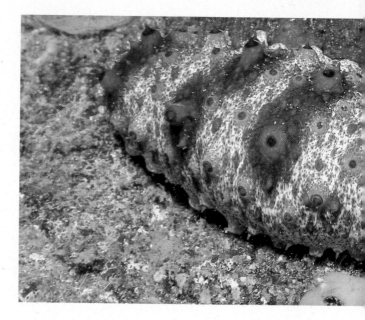

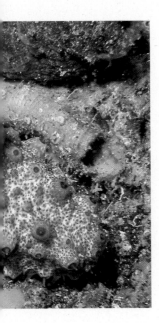

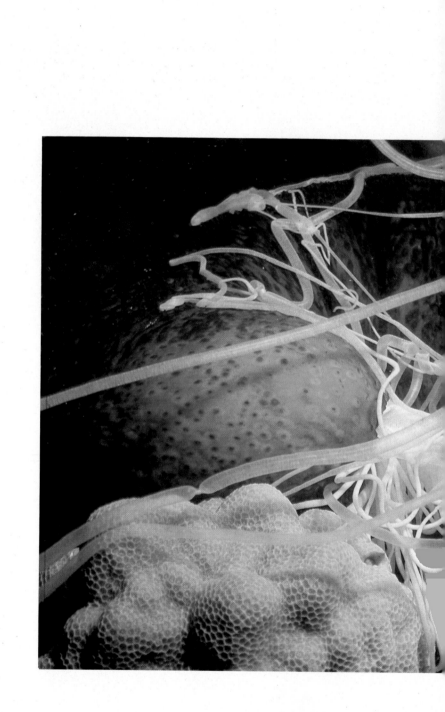

Sea cucumbers are slow moving creatures and have developed various means of defense. Some species eject long white sticky processes called Cuverian organs when molested, while other species may evert the entire digestive tract. Both structures grow back in time.

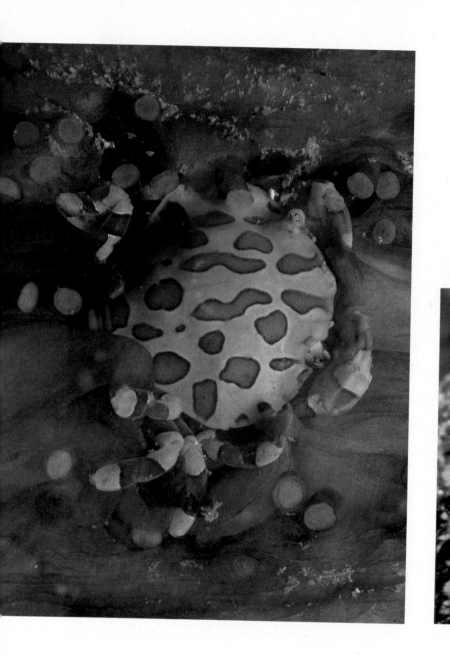

COMMENSALISM

mall swimming crab *Lissocarcinus orbicularis* lives with sea
nbers and may be found in the mouth, anus, or on the body of
species. It ranges in color from almost all black with white
to white with black spots, and is ½ to 1 inch in width.

CRUSTACEANS
Phylum Arthropoda

The crustaceans include the familiar barnacles, lobsters, shrimps, and crabs. They share the common characteristic of having jointed legs and a hard body

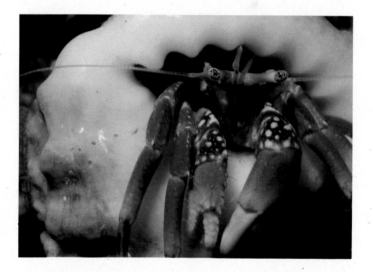

covering that must be molted or shed periodically in order for the animal to grow. Some crustaceans, such as the shrimps and lobsters, have a well developed abdomen which they use in swimming. In crabs, on the other hand, the abdomen, is reduced to a small flap on the underside of the body which covers the reproductive organs. (Above, *Calcinus latens.)*

BARBER POLE SHRIMP

Hawaii has several species of large, colorful shallow-water shrimp. One often seen by both reef walkers and scuba divers is the red and white banded shrimp *Stenopus hispidus*. The first three pairs of legs bear pincers, with the third pair being greatly enlarged. This third pair of legs can be easily dropped by the shrimp when alarmed or molested, much as a lizard is able to drop its tail. *S. hispidus* is usually found in male-female pairs, but is sometimes seen in a piggyback arrangement with a small individual sitting on the back of a larger one. When shrimp that were not found together are placed in an aquarium with each other, one will often kill the other. This species is found around the world in tropical seas and in some parts of the world has been reported to "clean" fish. The average size is 2 inches in length.

MANTIS SHRIMP

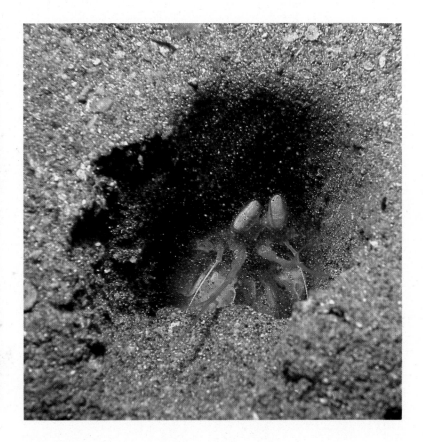

Although obviously crustaceans, the mantis shrimp differ from other members of this group in a number of characteristics: their gills are under the abdomen rather than near the front of the body; and their pincers, or raptorial appendages, fold like the blade of a jackknife. 'Alo 'alo, as the Hawaiians call them, lead a reclusive life, inhabiting burrows in the sand or in dead coral heads. They are generally solitary and aggressive carnivores. Their raptorial appendages are often not noticeable at first, as they fold up under the body. These appendages are modified depending on the food habits of the different species of mantis shrimp. Those that prey upon fish bear many spines along the appendage, while those that eat shelled invertebrates have the elbow modified for smashing and breaking. Mantis shrimp are extremely fast with these appendages and should not be picked up with bare hands. They are sometimes seen on shallow reef flats and range from 1 to 12 inches in length.

SNAPPING SHRIMP

The snapping shrimp are found around the world in the tropics. There are a great many species living in a wide variety of habitats, and each species has its own special place in the reef ecosystem. Some species are found only in live coral heads, some live in burrows in the sand with fish called gobies, others live in sponges or among coral rubble. One pincer is always larger than the other, and is specially modified to make a loud popping noise. Snapping shrimp are generally less than an inch in length.

HARLEQUIN SHRIMP

The harlequin shrimp *Hymenocera picta* is named for its gaudy coloration. This beautiful species is highly prized by aquarists, which may account for its relative scarcity. It feeds on sea stars and is found associated with them. This is not as bad for the starfish as it may seem, however, as starfish are able to regenerate lost body parts. Some starfish, such as *Linckia multifora*, are able to regenerate the entire body from a single arm. These shrimp are usually found below the intertidal zone and are about 1 inch in length.

LOBSTERS

Both the spiny and slipper lobsters lack the large claws found in the "Maine" lobster. Spiny lobsters (*ula,* below) are usually found under ledges or large rocks and can be spotted by their long, stout antennae. Slipper lobsters (*ula papa,* right) on the other hand, are often found in crevices and on the ceilings and walls of caves. At night they are sometimes found on the reef flat. Their flattened bodies and cryptic coloration allow them to blend in with their surroundings, and they are much less noticeable than the spiny lobster. Spiny lobsters may reach several pounds in weight. Slipper lobsters vary from small (3 inch) species to very large (18 inch) species. (Below, *Panulirus marginatus;* upper right, *Scyllarides squammosus;* lower right, *Arctides regalis.*)

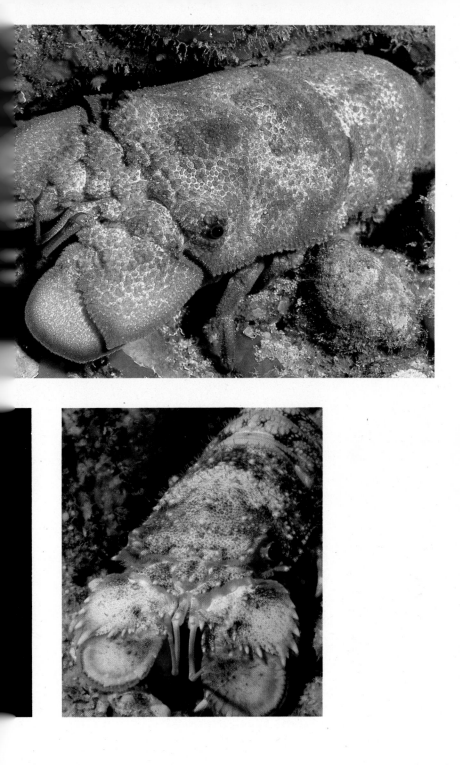

HERMIT CRABS

Hermit crabs demonstrate an unusual lifestyle. The abdomen has lost the protective hard covering and well-developed musculature found in the shrimp and lobsters, rendering them highly vulnerable to reef carnivores. Their habit of living in snail shells protects this soft abdomen and provides a convenient and portable refuge for the entire animal. Many species of hermit crab have one enlarged pincer, which they use as a door to seal off the opening to the shell. *Trizopagurus strigatus* (below) has a greatly flattened body suitable for inhabiting cone shells.

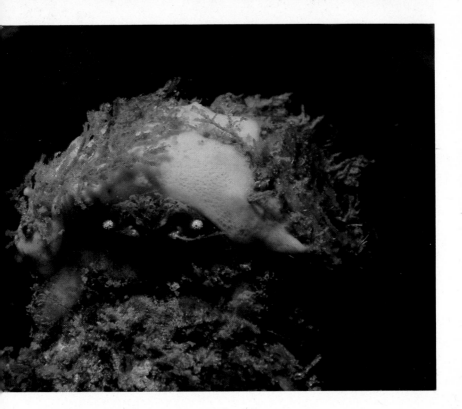

SPONGE CRABS

Sponge crabs gain their name from their habit of
carrying sponges, colonial tunicates, or zoanthids
on their backs. Species such as *Cryptodromiopsis
tridens* (above) may be quite small, (1 to 2 inches
across), while other species may be 8 to 10 inches
across. Small specimens may be red or brown,
while the larger ones are brown with white tipped
pincers. Both are found in shallow reef areas.
The sponge is attached to the body by the last pair
of legs which are elevated above the body. The
sponge serves to camouflage the crab.

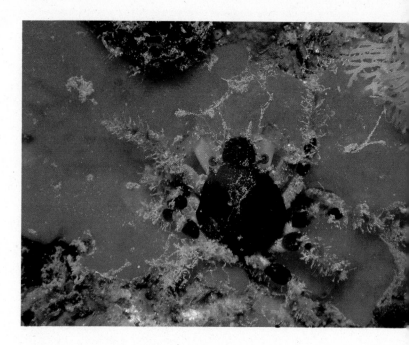

BOX CRABS

DECORATOR CRABS

Decorator crabs are small, spindly-legged crabs with a single or double rostrum (elongate process) between the eyes. This rostrum and much of the rest of the body are covered with tiny hooks. The crab picks up small pieces of algae, sponges, and hydroids and places them on the back where they are held by these hooks. Decorator crabs are common on algae-covered rocks on reef flats but are hard to find because they are so well camouflaged. They are usually less than an inch in length.

Box crabs (*poki poki*) live beneath the sand with only their sensory structures at the surface. Their eyes, antennae and respiratory openings are concentrated on the highest point of the domed carapace allowing the bulk of the crab to be hidden. This camouflage offers some protection from predators. The box crab is also very compact, with no stray legs sticking out to be grabbed by a fish. The carapace has winglike extensions on each side which cover the walking legs, and the large, flattened chelipeds (pincers) shield the front of the body. To obtain food, the box crab uses the curious knobs on one of the chelipeds to crush small shelled invertebrates. Box crabs average 3 inches in width. (Below and left, *Calappa hepatica*.)

GHOST CRABS

Animals living in social groups usually have some means of communication with each other, and ghost crabs are no exception. They create sound by rubbing a raised ridge on the inside of the palm against the base of the arm. They also communicate visually by the types of sand mounds and burro they build. A reproductively mature male of *Ocypode*

topthalmus will build a spiral burrow and set the pyramid-
ed sand mound a short distance from the burrow opening.
ales and juveniles do not build spiral burrows or well
ed sand mounds. Another visual signal is the horn at the
of the eyestalk of the reproductively mature males of
ode ceratopthalmus (top).
st crabs are called *ohiki* in Hawaiian and are used as live
for some types of fishing. They are most active at night.
t crabs are 2 inches in width.

XANTHID CRABS

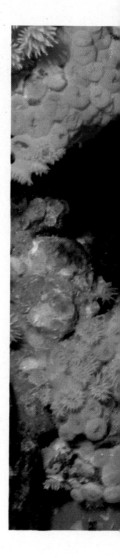

The xanthid (say "zan-thid") crabs are the largest family of crabs on Hawaiian reefs. Their bodies are oval in shape and broader than long. The chelipeds (pincers) are large in proportion to the body and the fingers are often black. These large chelipeds are used both for defense and for breaking open the shells of other animals for food. Xanthid crabs are often found in crevices on the reef where they wedge themselves in backwards with their strong, spine-tipped walking legs and face the world with eyes, antennae, and formidable claws.

There are many species of xanthid crabs, including the large "7-11" crab *Carpilius maculatus,* called *alakuma* in Hawaiian. A Hawaiian legend relates how this crab got its dark red spots. It was said that a sea god wished to eat it and grabbed it, but the crab pinched the god and drew blood. The god grabbed the crab three different times, leaving bloody fingerprints on the carapace each time until he was finally able to catch it.

Most xanthid crabs are small and generally
non-aggressive. They can be held in the palm of
the hand without danger and if placed on their
backs usually lie motionless with the legs held
close to the body. In some parts of the Pacific
certain species of xanthid crabs are poisonous when
eaten, and although there are Hawaiian legends
concerning poisonous *kumimi* crabs used in
sorcery, no species in Hawaii has yet been
scientifically proven to be poisonous. (Below,
Carpilodes supernodosus.)

Lybia edmondsoni is probably one of the most unusual of all the xanthid crabs, both in its appearance and in its unusual habit of carrying sea anemones around in its claws. When frightened, this species holds its anemones up like boxing gloves. This crab is small, usually about an inch in width. It can be found under rocks in the intertidal zone.

ROCK CRABS

Large numbers of the dark, fast-running *a'ama* crab, *Grapsus tenuicrustatus,* can usually be found in the upper-intertidal zone of rocky shorelines. Their molts, or discarded outer skeletons, are often seen among the shoreline rocks they inhabit, but are reddish in color rather than black. *A'ama* crabs are superbly adapted for living in a wave-battered environment. Their flattened bodies and long legs give a low center of gravity and broad base to meet the force of the waves. The flatness of the body allows the crabs to hide in narrow crevices, while spines on the tips of the legs help in grasping the rocks. Small pincers reduce weight and bulk and the dark color aids in camouflage. These crabs were used medicinally by early Hawaiians and are still used for food and bait.

SWIMMING CRABS

Swimming crabs are
easily recognized by their
paddle-shaped last pair of
legs. They are active,
aggressive crabs with sharply
pointed pincers and should
be handled with caution.
Many species bury
in the sand for protection.
Several of the larger species
such as the Samoan crab, the
Hawaiian crab, and the *Haole*
crab are popular for food.
(*Thalamita crenata,* above.)

SEA SQUIRTS
Phylum Chordata

Although often non-descript, the tunicates are very unusual animals. In the adult form they live attached to hard surfaces, drawing water in through one body opening and exhaling it through the other, superficially resembling sponges. Like the sponges they are filter

COLONIAL TUNICATES

Colonial tunicates are made up of many tiny sea-squirts embedded in common tissue. Their tiny siphons open on the surface forming a pattern of small pores. In some species each individual has its own separate incurrent and excurrent pore, while in others the excurrent pore may be shared by several individuals. In this case, it is usually larger than the incurrent pores.

These colonies may be flat and encrusting or large and bulbous, similar in size and shape to a "manapua". Colonial tunicates are filter feeders and are commonly found attached to pier pilings and the undersides of rocks in bays and harbors. They come in a wide variety of colors.

feeders. The common name "sea squirt" comes from the squirt-gunlike ability of solitary tunicates to eject a forceful stream of water when squeezed. They can be found under rocks in the intertidal zone and average 1 to 2 inches in height.

Tunicates are placed in the same phylum as humans. In the larval stage they have the chordate characters of gill slits and the forerunner of the vertebral column, the notochord. Even as adults they have a beating heart and a complete digestive tract.

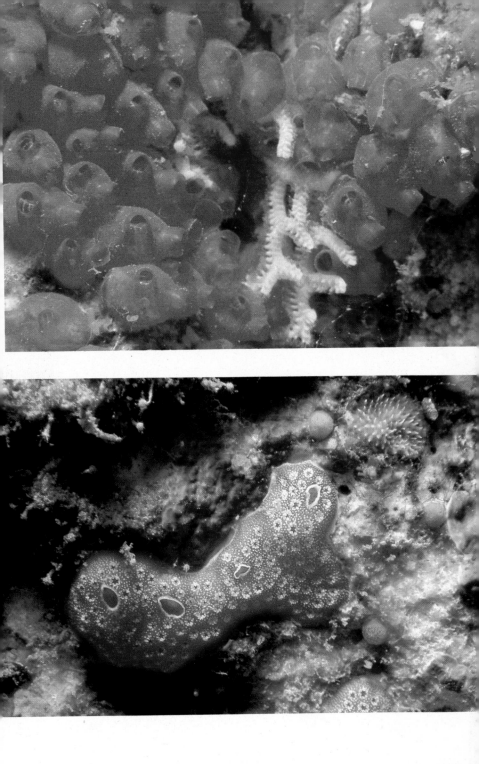

PHOTO CREDITS

ED ROBINSON

pages 2, 9, 10, 15, 17, 19, 20, 21, 23, 25, 26, 27, 28, 33, 35, 38, 43, 44, 55, 57, 59, 60, 62, 63, 64, 65, 67, 68, 69, 70, 73, 74 (top), 75, 76, 80, 82, 84, 86, 92 (top), 93, 94, 100, 103, back cover

SCOTT JOHNSON

pages cover, title page, 16, 20, 24, 30, 31, 32, 36, 37, 39, 40, 45, 46, 47, 48, 49 (bottom), 50 (bottom), 52, 53, 54, 58, 66, 73 (bottom), 77, 78, 79, 81, 83, 85, 88, 89 (top), 95, 96, 97, 98, 101, 102.

ART REED

pages 11, 12, 13, 14, 22, 29, 41, 42, 49 (top), 50 (top), 51, 56, 72, 87, 89 (bottom), 90, 92 (bottom).

ANN FIELDING

pages 3, 4, 8, 91.

ROB SHALLENBERGER

page 7.

LESLIE LYUM

pages 5, 6.

BRUCE CARLSON

page 71.

Special thanks to the Waikiki Aquarium and its director, Dr. Leighton Taylor for their support in the production of this book.

Thanks also to Mary Morioka for her art direction, to Ed Robinson, Scott Johnson, and Art Reed for their photographs, to Dr. Dennis Devaney of the Bishop Museum, Janet White, Dr. Bob Kinzie, and Carol Hopper of the University of Hawaii for help with animal identification, to Dr. Don Abbott for ecological information on sea urchins, to Drs. Rob and Ed Shallenberger for special help with the plankton photograph, and to Ruth Naftel for her typing.